The Heinle
PICTURE
DICTIONARY
for Children

Workbook

THOMSON

HEINLE ™

Australia • Canada • Mexico • Singapore • United Kingdom • United States

The Heinle PICTURE DICTIONARY for Children Workbook

Jill Korey O'Sullivan

Editorial Director: *Joe Dougherty*

Publisher: *Sherrise Roehr*

VP, Director of Content Development: *Anita Raducanu*

Development Editor: *John Hicks*

Director of Product Marketing: *Amy T. Mabley*

Executive Marketing Manager: *Jim McDonough*

Product Marketing Manager: *Katie Kelley*

International Marketing Manager: *Ian Martin*

Senior Content Project Manager: *Maryellen Killeen*

Content Project Manager: *Dawn Marie Elwell*

Asset Development Coordinator: *Noah Vincelette*

Associate Media Development Editor: *Jonelle Lonergan*

Senior Print Buyer: *Mary Beth Hennebury*

Freelance Development Editor: *Carol Crowell*

Project Management and Composition:
    InContext Publishing Partners

Cover Layout: *Lisa Mezikofsky*

Printer: *Quebecor World*

For permission to use material from this text or product,
submit a request online at http://www.thomsonrights.com

Any additional questions about permissions can be
submitted by email to thomsonrights@thomson.com

Student Edition
ISBN 13: 978-1-4240-0421-8
ISBN: 1-4240-0421-7

International Student Edition (softcover)
ISBN 13: 978-1-4240-0943-5
ISBN: 1-4240-0943-X
(Not for Sale in the United States)

Credits

Illustrators

Ron Carboni/Anita Grien (www.AnitaGrien.com) pp. 112, 124
Bruce Cayard/Anita Grien (www.AnitaGrien.com) Monkey flip animation
Adrian Chesterman/Artworks Illustration pp. 30, 52, 56 (top)
Mike Gardner pp. 3, 9, 12, 18, 20, 22, 39, 47, 55 (top), 65, 68, 75, 78, 89, 103, 106–107
Patrick Gnan/Deborah Wolfe Ltd. pp. 104, 108, 120, 121 (top), 122
Precision Graphics pp. 7 (balloons), 11, 14, 17 (bottom 1), 19 (bottom 3), 23 (bottom 2), 24, 25 (bottom 1), 27 (sun, moon), 29, 36, 37 (C), 38, 40, 45, 54, 74, 76, 79, 84 (top), 88, 95 (top 6), 99, 114, 121 (chart art), 125
Sharon and Joel Harris/Deborah Wolfe Ltd. pp. 110–111 (B)
InContext pp. 2, 4, 7 (shapes), 58, 109, 126 (4)
Bob Kayganich/Deborah Wolfe Ltd. pp. 5, 8, 127
Jonathan Massie/Wilkinson Studios, Inc. pp. 43–44, 59, 90 (top), 91, 92, 94, 95 (bottom 6), 98, 100–101
Daniel O'Leary/Illustration Ltd. pp. 16, 17 (top 6), 62–63
Simon Shaw/Deborah Wolfe Ltd. pp. 6, 25 (clowns), 32, 67, 73, 81, 84 (bottom 5), 85, 86–87, 111 (C), 115
Ralph Voltz/Deborah Wolfe Ltd. pp. 34 (boy), 35 (art in chart), 50, 60

Photos

Unit One UNIT ICON CREDIT: ©InContext Publishing Partners; 7 (blackboard, cone): ©Photolibrary Group; (window): ©Jupiterimages; (pizza): ©Hemera Photo-Objects; 10 (1): ©Image Source Pink/Alamy; 10 (2): ©Philip Scalia/Alamy; 10 (3): ©Hot Ideas/Photolibrary Group; 10 (4, 6): ©Jupiterimages; 10 (5): ©DAJ/Getty Images

Unit Two UNIT ICON CREDIT: ©Corbis Collection/Alamy; 15 (1, 3, 5 r.): ©Jupiterimages; 15 (2 l., 5 r.): ©Image Source Pink/Getty Images; 15 (2 r.): ©ImageDJ/Photolibrary Group; 15 (4 r., 5 l.): ©PhotoAlto/Alamy; 19 (2): ©Hemera Photo-Objects; 19 (5): ©Photos.com Select/Photolibrary Group; 19 (6): ©Thomas Northcut/PhotoDisc/Getty Images; 21 (hat, scarf): ©D. Hurst/Alamy; 21 (boot): ©Keith Levit Photography/Photolibrary Group; 21 (glove, sandal): ©Hemera Photo-Objects; 21 (shoe): ©Royalty-Free/Corbis

Unit Three UNIT ICON CREDIT: ©Photographer's Choice/Peter Gridley/Getty Images; most 28: ©Hemera Photo-Objects; 28 (fridge): ©C Squared Studios/Photodisc/Getty Images; 29 (1, 5): ©Hemera Photo-Objects; 29 (2): ©Photolibrary Group; 29 (3): ©sciencephotos/Alamy; 29 (4): ©Jupiterimages; 31 (1, 3, 4, 5 r., 6 r.): ©Jupiterimages; 31 (2 l.): ©Rob Walls/Alamy; 31 (2 r.): ©photolibrary.com pty. ltd./Photolibrary Group; 31 (5 l.): ©ICHIRO/Digital Vision/Getty Images; 31 (6 l.): ©Judith Collins/Alamy; 33 (closet): ©Jason Homa/Digital Vision/Getty Images; 33 (toy box): ©Andy Crawford/Dorling Kindersley/Getty Images; 33 (blanket): ©Siede Preis/Photodisc/Getty Images; 33 (rug, dresser, pillow, curtains): ©Jupiterimages; 33 (hanger): ©Peter Dazeley/Photographer's Choice RF/Getty Images; 33 (bear, lamp): ©Photolibrary Group; 33 (cat): ©photolibrary.com pty. ltd./Photolibrary Group; most 34: ©Hemera Photo-Objects; 34 (showerhead): ©David Buffington/Photodisc/Getty Images; 34 (towel): ©photolibrary.com pty. ltd./Photolibrary Group; most 35: ©Hemera Photo-Objects; 35 (shampoo): ©Photodisc Collection/Getty; 35 (showerhead): ©David Buffington/Photodisc/Getty Images; 35 (mirror): ©Jupiterimages; 35 (bathmat, towel, toilet) ©photolibrary.com pty. ltd./Photolibrary Group; 37 (treehouse): ©Yellow Dog Productions/Digital Vision/Getty Images; 37 (driveway): ©Photolibrary Group; 37 (key) ©Hemera Photo-Objects; 37 (wagon): ©C Squared Studios/Photodisc/Getty Images; 37 (B fence): ©Jupiterimages; 37 (C fence): ©Image Source Pink/Image Source/Getty Images; 37 (roof, house): ©Hemera Photo-Objects; 38 (brush, battery): ©Hemera Photo-Objects; 38 (tape measure): ©Siede Preis/Photodisc Green/Getty; 38 (ladder): ©Jupiterimages; 39 (hammer, brush): ©Hemera Photo-Objects; 39 (washer, dryer): ©Corbis Collection/Alamy; 39 (paint): ©Patrick Olear/PhotoEdit; 39 (nail): ©John Coletti

Unit Four UNIT ICON CREDIT: ©Iconica/Ross M Horowitz/Getty Images; 41 (wheelchair): ©Hemera Photo-Objects; 41 (boat): ©IndexOpen/RF; 41 (skateboard): ©Jupiterimages; 41 (airplane): ©Stockbyte/Getty Images; 41 (train): ©Photodisc Green/Getty Images; 42 (flowers, fire hydrant): ©Hemera Photo-Objects; 42 (bread, gas, florist, factory): ©Jupiterimages; 42 (money): ©John Coletti; 42 (stamps): ©Brand X Pictures; 42 (groceries): ©Stockbyte/Getty Images; 42 (supermarket): ©Steve Lewis/Digital Vision/Getty Images; 42 (street): ©Chris Selby/Alamy; 42 (school): ©Thomas Barwick/Digital Vision/Getty Images; most 45: ©Jupiterimages; 45 (sandbox): ©imagebroker/Alamy; 45 (ball, statue): ©Hemera Photo-Objects; 45 (slide): ©Stefan Sollfors/Alamy; most 46: ©Jupiterimages; 46 (jungle gym): ©Brian Atkinson/Alamy; 46 (wagon): ©C Squared Studios/Photodisc/Getty Images; 46 (jump rope): ©Photolibrary Group; 46 (Frisbee): ©Nikreates/Alamy; most 47: ©Jupiterimages; 47 (kicking): ©Thomas Northcut/Digital Vision/Getty Images; 47 (throwing): ©Rich Reid/National Geographic/Getty Images; 47 (swinging): ©IndexOpen/RF; 49 (video): ©C Squared Studios/Photodisc/Getty Images; 49 (DVD): ©IndexOpen/RF; 49 (bookshelf): ©photolibrary.com pty. ltd./Photolibrary Group; most 51: ©Hemera Photo-Objects; 51 (dog): ©GK Hart/Vikki Hart/Photodisc/Getty Images; 51 (goldfish): ©photolibrary.com pty. ltd./Photolibrary Group; 51 (cat): ©Melissa Goodrum; 53 (money, shoe): ©Jupiterimages; 53 (meal, phone): ©Hemera Photo-Objects; 53 (tickets): ©Siede Preis/Photodisc/Getty Images; 53 (escalator): ©photolibrary.com pty. ltd./Photolibrary Group; 53 (elevator): ©Riko Pictures/Photodisc/Getty Images; 53 (bag): ©Photolibrary Group; 53 (shopper): ©George Doyle/Stockbyte/Getty Images; most 56: ©Hemera Photo-Objects; 56 (playpen): ©C Squared Studios/Photodisc/Getty Images; 56 (wipes): ©graficart.net/Alamy; 56 (potty chair): ©Gary Roebuck/Alamy; 57 (rattle): ©D. Hurst/Alamy; 57 (playpen): ©C Squared Studios/Photodisc/Getty Images; 57 (diaper): ©Jupiterimages; 57 (baby): ©David Young-Wolff/PhotoEdit; 57 (stroller): ©Hemera Photo-Objects; 59 (ladder): ©C Squared Studios/Photodisc/Getty Images; 59 (tape measure): ©Siede Preis/Photodisc Green/Getty; 59 (hammer, nail): ©Hemera Photo-Objects; 59 (shovel, saw): ©Jupiterimages; most 61: ©Jupiterimages; 61 (medicine, syringe): ©Hemera Photo-Objects; 61 (stethoscope): ©photolibrary.com pty. ltd./Photolibrary Group; 61 (scale, chart): ©JUPITERIMAGES/Brand X/Alamy; 63 (thermometer): ©Royalty-Free/Corbis; 64 (medicine, plunger, handcuffs, microscope, hammer): ©Hemera Photo-Objects; 64 (scissors, truck): ©Jupiterimages; 64 (firehouse): ©Stockbyte/Getty Images; 64 (dental office): ©Andersen Ross/Digital Vision/Getty Images; 64 (plane): ©James Lauritz/Digital Vision/Getty Images; 64 (theater): ©Tony Weller/Digital Vision/Getty Images; 64 (bakery): ©Dick Luria/Photodisc/Getty Images

Unit Five UNIT ICON CREDIT: ©Jamie Grill/Corbis; most 66: ©Jupiterimages; 66 (trash): ©Jules Frazier/Photodisc/Getty Images; 66 (backpack): ©Siede Preis/Photodisc/Getty Images; 66 (blackboard): ©Photolibrary Group; 66 (chalk): ©Stockbyte/Getty Images; most 67: ©Jupiterimages; 67 (chalk): ©Stockbyte/Getty Images; most 69: ©Jupiterimages; 69 (arm): ©Siede Preis/Photodisc/Getty Images; 69 (pen): ©Hemera Photo-Objects; 70 (pencil case): ©Stockdisc/Corbis; 70 (pen): ©Redfx/Alamy; 70 (folder): ©Mode Images Limited/Alamy; 70 (pencil, sharpener, paper, binder, eraser, stapler, calculator): ©2007 JupiterImages Corporation; 70 (money): ©Photodisc Green/PhotoLink/Getty Images; 70 (report card): ©Jeffrey Coolidge/Corbis; 70 (notebook): ©Brand X Pictures/Alamy; 70 (textbook, ruler): ©Photodisc Green/Ryan McVay/Getty Images; 71 (eraser, binder, calculator, pencil, stapler): ©2007 JupiterImages Corporation; 71 (pencil case): ©Stockdisc/Corbis; 71 (money): ©Photodisc Green/PhotoLink/Getty Images; 71 (notebook): ©Brand X Pictures/Alamy; 71 (pen): ©Redfx/Alamy; most 72: ©Jupiterimages; 72 (Joe): ©Ron Neubauer/Photo Edit, Inc.; 72 (markers): ©Siede Preis/Photodisc/Getty Images; 72 (glue): ©D. Hurst/Alamy; 72 (crayons): ©Stockbyte/Getty Images; 72 (pencil): ©2007 JupiterImages Corporation; 72 (paintbrush): ©Hemera Photo-Objects; most 73: ©Jupiterimages; 73 (brush, paper): ©Hemera Photo-Objects; 73 (crayons): ©Stockbyte/Getty Images; 74 (trumpet, violin, flute): ©Hemera Photo-Objects; 74 (xylophone): ©Jupiterimages; 74 (guitar, tambourine): ©Photodisc Collection/Getty; 74 (triangle): ©Peter Dazeley/Photographer's Choice RF/Getty Images

Unit Six UNIT ICON CREDIT: ©Stockbyte/Corbis; 76 (fruit bowl): ©Jupiterimages; 76 (grapes): ©Photodisc Collection/Getty Images; 76 (orange): ©2007 JupiterImages Corporation; 77 (banana, orange, mango, pear, plum, lemon, peach): ©Burke-Triolo Productions/Getty Images; 77 (raspberries, avocado, kiwi, pineapple, melon, papaya): ©2007 JupiterImages Corporation; 77 (blueberries): ©Royalty-Free/Corbis; 77 (raisins): ©Keith Seaman/FoodPix; 77 (apple): ©Photodisc Collection/Getty Images; most 79: ©Hemera Photo-Objects; 79 (green beans, corn, broccoli): ©2007 JupiterImages Corporation; 79 (peas): ©Craig Orsini/Index Stock Imagery Inc.; 80 (cereal, fork, spoon, knife): ©Jupiterimages; 80 (jam): ©Pick and Mix Images/Alamy; 80 (spaghetti, salad): ©Hemera Photo-Objects; 80 (butter): ©Comstock Images/Alamy; 80 (soup): ©foodfolio/Alamy; 80 (salt, pepper): ©D.Hurst/Alamy; 80 (noodles): ©Ingram Publishing/Alamy; 80 (fish): ©2007 Jupiter Images Corporation; 80 (sugar): ©Foodcollection.com/Alamy; 80 (honey): ©StockFood Creative/Lew Robertson/Getty Images; 80 (pasta): ©Andrew Twort/Alamy; 80 (chicken): ©Paul Springett/Alamy; 80 (steak): ©Gabe Palmer/Alamy; most 81: ©Hemera Photo-Objects; 81 (jam): ©Pick and Mix Images/Alamy; 81 (cheese, bread, rice): ©2007 JupiterImages Corporation; 81 (chicken): ©Paul Springett/Alamy; 81 (cereal): ©Jupiterimages; 81 (sugar): ©Foodcollection.com/Alamy; 81 (butter): ©Comstock Images/Alamy; 81 (salt): ©D.Hurst/Alamy; 81 (nuts): ©Photographer's Choice/Kevin Summers/Getty Images; 82 (Yumiko, Allen, fries, hamburger): ©Jupiterimages; 82 (sandwich, cookie): ©2007 JupiterImages Corporation; 82 (Carmen): ©Somos/Veer/Somos/Getty Images; 82 (David): ©Nancy Brown/Photodisc/Getty Images; 82 (Chim): ©Red Chopsticks/redchopsticks/Getty Images; 82 (chocolate): ©Ingram Publishing/Alamy; 82 (Sarah, Emil): ©rubberball/Rubberball Productions/Getty Images; 82 (taco): ©Stockdisc/Corbis; 82 (pie): ©Photodisc/Getty Images; 82 (Mary): ©Stockbyte/Getty Images; 82 (pizza): ©Barry Wong/Digital Vision/Getty Images; most 83: ©Hemera Photo-Objects; 83 (milk): ©2007 www.indexopen.com; 83 (soda): ©Comstock Premium/Alamy

Unit Seven UNIT ICON CREDIT: ©Taxi/Stephanie Rausser/Getty Images; 89 (boat, dinosaur): ©Jupiterimages; 89 (dice, game): ©Hemera Photo-Objects; 89 (doll): ©Erin Garvey/Index Stock Imagery, Inc.; 89 (blocks): ©Stockbyte/Getty Images; 89 (bubbles): ©Ablestock/Alamy; 89 (doll house): ©photolibrary.com pty. ltd./Photolibrary Group; most 90: ©Jupiterimages; 90 (candies): ©David Toase/Photodisc/Getty Images; 90 (candle): ©Stockdisc Classic/Alamy; 90 (lollipop): ©VStock LLC/Photolibrary Group; most 93: ©Jupiterimages; 93 (island): ©C Squared Studios/Photodisc/Getty Images; 93 (shell): ©Photodisc/Getty Images; 93 (sandcastle): ©JUPITERIMAGES/Creatas/Alamy; 93 (wave): ©Bill Romerhaus/Photolibrary Group; 97 (1): ©Hemera Photo-Objects; 97 (2, 3): ©Jupiterimages; 97 (4): ©SuperStock/Alamy; 97 (5): ©Siede Preis/Photodisc/Getty Images; 97 (6): ©COMSTOCK Images; most 99: ©Hemera Photo-Objects; 99 (pig): ©Digital Zoo/Digital Vision/Getty Images; 99 (chicken): ©GK Hart/Vikki Hart/Photodisc/Getty Images; 99 (goat): ©Jupiterimages; 99 (bull): ©C Edwards/Alamy; 99 (farm): ©David R. Frazier Photolibrary, Inc./Alamy; most 102: ©Hemera Photo-Objects; 102 (puck): ©Jupiterimages; 102 (racket): ©Hugh Threlfall/Alamy; most 103: ©Hemera Photo-Objects; 103 (puck, hockey stick): ©Jupiterimages; 103 (hoop): ©C Squared Studios/Photodisc/Getty Images; 103 (tennis net): ©PEPE/Alamy; 103 (goalpost): ©Corbis Premium Collection/Alamy

Unit Eight UNIT ICON CREDIT: ©Klaus Hackenberg/zefa/Corbis; most 105: ©Jupiterimages; 105 (watering can): ©Image Source Black/Image Source/Getty Images; 105 (grass): ©Photos.com/RF; 105 (puddle): ©Image Source Pink/Image Source/Getty Images; most 111: ©Hemera Photo-Objects; 111 (snowman): ©Steve Smith/Photographer's Choice RF/Getty Images; 111 (tree): ©Jupiterimages; most 112: ©Hemera Photo-Objects; 112 (ladybug): ©Nic Hamilton/Alamy; 112 (spider): ©JUPITERIMAGES/Brand X/Alamy; 112 (worm): ©JUPITERIMAGES/IT Stock Free/Alamy; 112 (bee): ©Stefan Sollfors/Alamy; most 113: ©Hemera Photo-Objects; 113 (ladybug): ©Nic Hamilton/Alamy; 113 (bee, wasp): ©Stefan Sollfors/Alamy; 113 (cocoon): ©Scott Camazine/Alamy; 113 (snail): ©Jupiterimages; 113 (fly): ©John Foxx/Stockbyte/Getty Images; 113 (tick): ©imagebroker/Alamy; 113 (moth): ©sciencephotos/Alamy; most 115: ©Hemera Photo-Objects; 115 (wing): ©Glenn Mitsui/Getty Images; 115 (bat): ©Paul Springett/Alamy; most 116: ©Hemera Photo-Objects; 116 (ostrich): ©Eureka/Alamy; 119: ©Hemera Photo-Objects; most 120: ©Hemera Photo-Objects; 120 (nest): ©Foodcollection/Getty Images; 120 (robin): ©John Anderson/Alamy; 120 (mouse): ©Digital Zoo/Digital Vision/Getty Images; 120 (deer): ©Photos.com/RF; 120 (toad): ©Reimar Gaertner/Alamy; most 123: ©Hemera Photo-Objects; 123 (fox): ©PhotoAlto/Alamy; 123 (walrus): ©Index Stock/Alamy; 123 (puffin, grizzly, cub, moose): ©Jupiterimages; 123 (antler): ©Stocksearch/Alamy; 123 (Eskimo): ©Picture Contact/Alamy; 123 (igloo): ©Yvette Cardozo/Index Stock Imagery Inc.; most 125: ©Hemera Photo-Objects; 125 (2): ©Joel Sartore/National Geographic/Getty Images; 125 (3): ©David Hiser/Photodisc/Getty Images; 125 (6): ©Joel Sartore/National Geographic/Getty Images; 126 (1): Courtesy of NASA; 126 (3): ©Jupiterimages; 126 (5): ©Photodisc Red/Getty Images; 126 (6): ©Digital Vision/Getty Images; 126 (7): ©Comstock/Fotosearch; 126 (8): ©Stockdisc Classic/Alamy; 127: ©Digital Vision/Getty Images

Contents

Aa	Ee	Ii	Mm	Qq	Uu	Yy
Bb	Ff	Jj	Nn	Rr	Vv	Zz
Cc	Gg	Kk	Oo	Ss	Ww	
Dd	Hh	Ll	Pp	Tt	Xx	

A Connect the dots. Write the letter.

B
C· ·A
D· ·F
E

___C___

B
C· ·A
D· ·E
H· ·F
G

_____

A·
B· ·C

_____

A· ·C
B

_____

B D
A C E

_____

A C E
B D

_____

A __B__ C ____ E ____ G ____ I ____ K ____ M

____ O ____ Q ____ S ____ U ____ W ____ Y ____

C Write the names in ABC order.

1. _____Amir_____

2. _____

3. _____

4. _____

5. _____

6. _____

7. _____

8. _____

D Write your name.

_____

3

Numbers

one	seven	thirteen	nineteen	fourth
two	eight	fourteen	twenty	fifth
three	nine	fifteen		
four	ten	sixteen	first	plus
five	eleven	seventeen	second	equal
six	twelve	eighteen	third	minus

A **Connect the dots. Write the numbers.**

B
A•   •C
    •D
 E•
F•   •G

_____2_____

A•
B•   •H
C•   •G
D•   •F
   E

_____

B
A•   •C
    •D
E•   •F
    •G
İ   H

_____

A   B
•   •

   •C

Ḋ

_____

B   A
•   •
   D•
C•   •E
    •F
İ   •G
 H

_____

Ċ
D•   •B
E•   A•G
  F•   •H
    •I

_____

4

B **Write the number or the word.**

one ___1___   seven _____

two _____   eight _____

three _____   _____ 9

_____ 4   _____ 10

five _____   plus _____

_____ 6   _____ =

C **Count the toys. Write the number.**

 ___6___   _____   _____

 _____   _____   _____

 _____   _____   _____

 _____

Colors and Shapes

black	orange	yellow	square
blue	pink		star
brown	purple	circle	triangle
gray	red	heart	
green	white	rectangle	

A **Write the missing shape or color.**

1. The triangle is _____ blue _____.

2. The square is _____.

3. The _____ is green.

4. The _____ is yellow.

5. The rectangle is _____.

6. The _____ is brown.

B **Write the shape.**

1. __circle__

2. _____

3. _____

4. _____

5. _____ **and** _____

C **Unscramble the words. Color the balloons.**

pnik

4. _____

owllye

1. __yellow__

uebl

3. _____

georan

2. _____

plerpu

energ

7. _____

der

5. _____

6. _____

7

In, On, Over

above	between	on	under
across from	down	on the left of	up
around	in	on the right of	
behind	in front of	over	
below	next to	through	

A **Look at the picture. Write the missing word.**

1. The dog ran _____**through**_____ a gate.

2. He jumped _____ a cow.

3. He ran _____ 2 horses.

4. He is running _____ a tree.

5. The cat is running _____ the tree.

B (Circle) the correct spelling.

1. (over)　　　ohver　　　owver

2. undar　　　unnder　　　under

3. behind　　　beehind　　　bahind

4. between　　　beetween　　　betwin

5. arond　　　ahround　　　around

C (Circle) *Yes* or *No.*

I am **in** my classroom now.	(Yes)	No
I am sitting **on** the floor.	Yes	No
I am sitting **on** a chair.	Yes	No
My friend is **next to** me.	Yes	No
My teacher is **across from** me.	Yes	No

Opposites

big	fast	old	slow
clean	long	open	small
closed	loud	quiet	tall
dirty	new	short	young

A (Circle) the correct word.

1. young   (old)

2. long   short

3. clean   dirty

4. open   closed

5. fast   slow

6. tall   short

B **Read and draw what's missing.**

1. Ben is happy.

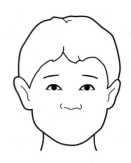

2. Ben is sad.

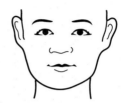

3. Sharon's hair is short.

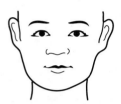

4. Sharon's hair is long.

5. Emilio's eyes are open.

6. Emilio's eyes are closed.

C **Circle** *Yes* or *No*.

1. Is your hair long?	Yes	No
2. Are you short?	Yes	No
3. Are your shoes dirty?	Yes	No
4. Is your school small?	Yes	No
5. Is your class quiet?	Yes	No

Time

afternoon	watch	Wednesday	May
calendar	week	Thursday	June
clock		Friday	July
day	one o'clock	Saturday	August
evening	one fifteen	Sunday	September
hour	one thirty		October
minute	one forty-five	January	November
month		February	December
morning	Monday	March	
night	Tuesday	April	

A When do you do it? Check (✓).

	morning	afternoon	evening	night
go to school	✓			
watch TV				
sleep				
brush teeth				
do homework				

B **Write the time.**

1. _1:00_ **2.** _____ **3.** _____ **4.** _____

C **Complete the sentences. Write the missing words.**

1. I stay home from school on these days:

_____**Saturday**_____ and _____**Sunday**_____.

2. I go to school on these days: _____,

_____, _____,

_____, _____.

3. My birthday is in this month: _____.

4. There are only 28 days most of the time in

_____.

5. There are 7 days in a _____.

D **Complete the words. Write the missing letters. Write the days in order of time.**

1. W __e__ dn __e__ sd __a__ y   **1.** _____

2. S ____ t ____ rd ____ y   **2.** _____

3. S ____ nd ____ y   **3.** _____**Wednesday**_____

4. M ____ nd ____ y   **4.** _____

5. Th ____ rsd ____ y   **5.** _____

6. Fr ____ d ____ y   **6.** _____

7. Tu ____ sd ____ y   **7.** _____

Face and Hair

braces   ear   hair   ponytail
braid   eye   long   short
cheek   eyebrow   mouth   straight
chin   forehead nose   tongue
curly   glasses   pigtail   tooth

A **What is missing? Draw it and write the word.**

1. ___mouth___

2. _____

3. _____

4. _____

5. _____

6. _____

B **Which word in each line doesn't belong? Circle the word.**

1. short   (ear)   long

2. nose   pigtail   ponytail

3. straight   braid   curly

4. chin   eye   eyebrow

5. braces   glasses   long

C Complete the words. (Circle) the correct picture.

 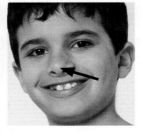

1. __c__ __h__ eek

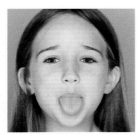 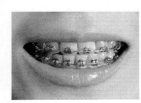    

2. ____ ____ aces   3. ____ ____ in

4. ____ ____ aid   5. ____ ____ ____aight

D (Circle) *Yes* or *No*.

1. I have brown hair.   Yes   No

2. I have blue eyes.   Yes   No

3. I have short hair.   Yes   No

4. I have curly hair.   Yes   No

5. I wear glasses.   Yes   No

Body

ankle	chest	foot	heel	neck	thumb
arm	elbow	hand	knee	shoulder	toe
back	finger	head	leg	stomach	wrist

A **What is he touching? Write the word.**

1. _____ toe _____

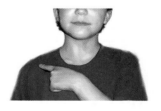

2. _____

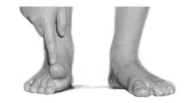

3. _____

4. _____

5. _____

6. _____

7. _____

8. _____

16

B Say the word. Circle the first letter.

1. (h)   g   l

2. b   f   o

3. k   b   n

4. c   b   l

5. p   l   r

6. s   b   t

C Complete the drawing. Write the words.

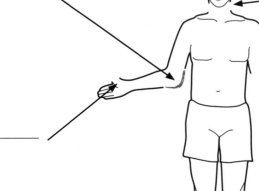

1. ___elbow___   4. _____

2. _____   5. _____

3. _____   6. _____

belt	jeans	skirt	underpants
blouse	jewelry	sneaker	undershirt
bracelet	necklace	sweatshirt	underwear
earrings	ring	tights	
jacket	shorts	T-shirt	

A **Unscramble the words. Write.**

1. jeywelr

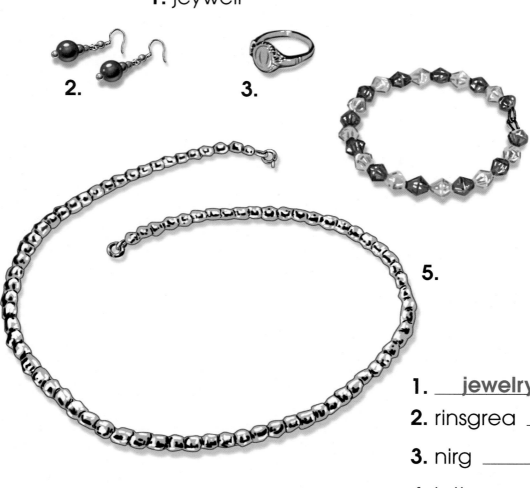

2.

3.

4.

5.

1. __jewelry__

2. rinsgrea _____

3. nirg _____

4. letbrace _____

5. neckacle _____

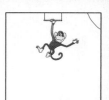

B **Write the missing letters.**

| br | ~~bl~~ | sk | sh | sw | sn |

1. _b_ _l_ ouse

2. ____ ____ acelet

3. ____ ____ orts

4. ____ ____ irt

5. ____ ____ eakers

6. ____ ____ eatshirt

C **Write *Yes*, *No*, or *Both*.**

	Girls	Boys	Both
skirt	Yes	No	
shorts			Both
T-shirt			
ring			
tights			
jeans			
jacket			

Clothes 2

baseball cap	dress	raincoat	sleeve
boot	glove	sandal	sock
button	hat	scarf	sweater
coat	pants	shirt	tie
collar	pocket	shoe	umbrella

A **What is the boy wearing? Write the words on the picture.**

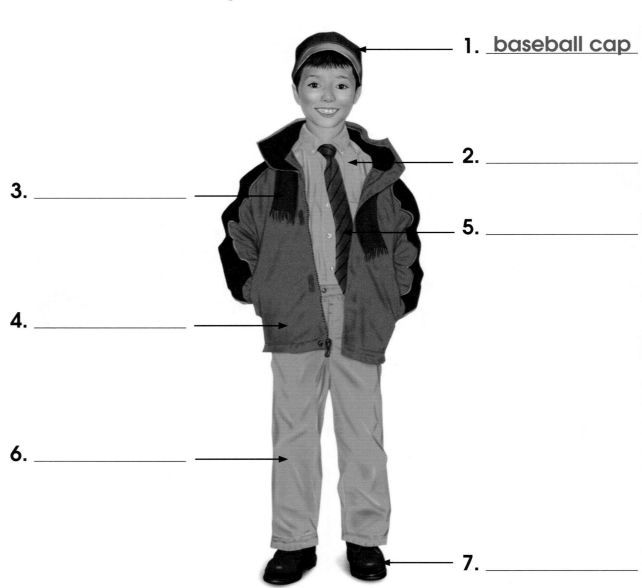

1. <u>baseball cap</u>

2. _____

3. _____

4. _____

5. _____

6. _____

7. _____

B (Circle) the three best things to wear.

1. coat   raincoat   sandals

    scarf   dress   gloves

2. coat   raincoat   boots

    umbrella   sandals   tie

C **What do you wear on these parts of the body? Write the words.**

baseball cap				

My Family

aunt	father	grandpa	mother
brother	grandfather	grandparents	parents
cousin	grandma	me	sister
dad	grandmother	mom	uncle

A Write the word for each person.

1. _____sister_____   4. _____

2. _____   5. _____

3. _____   6. _____

B Write the words from Activity A in the chart.

Boys and Men	Girls and Women
father	

C Answer the questions about Reiko's family.

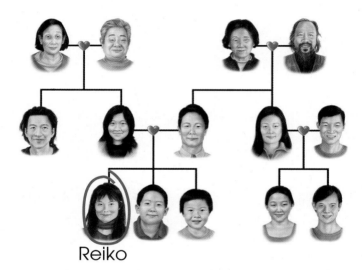

Reiko

1. How many grandparents does Reiko have? ____four____

2. How many grandmothers does Reiko have? _____

3. How many parents does Reiko have? _____

4. How many brothers does Reiko have? _____

5. How many sisters does Reiko have? _____

6. How many aunts does Reiko have? _____

7. How many uncles does Reiko have? _____

8. How many cousins does Reiko have? _____

Feelings

happy	scared	cry	laugh
hungry	silly	drink	smile
mad	thirsty	eat	yawn
sad	tired	hide	yell

A the correct face.

1. mad

2. silly

3. tired

4. sad

5. happy

6. scared

B Look at the pictures. Write the word for the action.

1. _____yell_____   2. _____   3. _____

4. _____   5. _____   6. _____

C How do you feel today? Draw your face. Write the word for your feeling.

Today I feel _____.

My Day

brush my teeth
call my friend
clean my room
come home
do my homework
eat breakfast
eat dinner

eat lunch
get dressed
get up
go to bed
go to school
hug my dad
kiss my mom

make my bed
play with friends
sleep
take a shower
watch TV

A **What is the boy doing? Write.**

1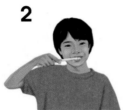

2

3

4

5

6

7

8

1. __The boy gets up.__

2. _____

3. _____

4. _____

5. _____

6. _____

7. _____

8. _____

B Match and write the word.

to school
up
to bed
breakfast
~~a shower~~
dressed
dinner

take _____ a shower _____

get _____

get _____

eat _____

eat _____

go _____

go _____

C Do you do it during the day or at night? Write.

☀	🌙
I hug my dad.	I hug my dad.

27

In the Kitchen

cabinet   microwave   refrigerator   cook
counter   oven   stove   wash the dishes
drawer   pan
kettle   pot   toaster

A   **Write the words.**

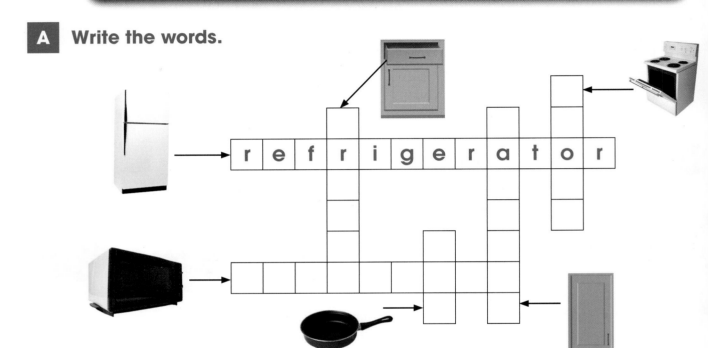

r e f r i g e r a t o r

B   **Write the missing letter: *a, e, i, o,* or *u.***

1. k __e__ ttle   **2.** p ____ t   **3.** st ____ ve

4. p ____ n   **5.** cab ____ net   **6.** toast ____ r

C **What do you use to cook it?** **Circle.**

1. toaster   oven   (kettle)

2. pan   microwave   oven

3. pot   kettle   pan

4. toaster   pot   kettle

5. toaster   microwave   stove

D **Do you cook? Do you wash the dishes? Ask your friends. Write *Yes* or *No*.**

Name	Do you . . .	Do you . . .
Me (name)		
_____ (name)		
_____ (name)		

29

armchair	DVD player	lamp	telephone
CD player	earphones	light	television
ceiling	fire	picture	vase
coffee table	fireplace	plant	wall
couch	floor	rug	

A **Look at the picture. Read the sentences. Circle *True* or *False*.**

		True	False
1. The couch is blue.		True	(False)
2. The rug is under the couch.		True	False
3. The rug is red.		True	False
4. The girl is on the floor.		True	False
5. There is a lamp on the coffee table.		True	False
6. There is a picture on the wall.		True	False
7. The television is large.		True	False
8. There is a fire in the fireplace.		True	False

B Say the words. Do they start with the same sound? Circle *Yes* or *No*.

1. Yes / No

2. Yes / No

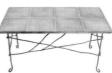 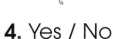

3. Yes / No

4. Yes / No

5. Yes / No

6. Yes / No

C Check (✓) the things you have in your living room.

☐ armchair
☐ CD player
☐ ceiling
☐ coffee table
☐ couch
☐ DVD player
☐ earphones

☐ fire
☐ fireplace
☐ floor
☐ lamp
☐ light
☐ picture
☐ plant

☐ rug
☐ telephone
☐ television
☐ vase
☐ wall

In the Bedroom

alarm clock	closet	hanger	sheet
bed	comforter	lamp	slipper
blanket	curtain	pajamas	stuffed animals
carpet	dresser	pillow	toy box

A Read and color.

1. The blanket is blue.

2. The pillow is yellow.

3. The stuffed animals are brown.

4. The curtain is pink.

5. The carpet is green.

6. The slippers are orange.

B Circle the word that doesn't belong.

1. closet   hanger   (alarm clock)

2. blanket   lamp   pillow

3. comforter   stuffed animal toy box

4. bed   dresser   carpet

5. pajamas   dresser   slipper

C Which words end with the letter *t?* Check (✓) the words.

 ✓

 ☐

☐

 ☐

 ☐

 ☐

 ☐

☐

D Ask your friends: What things are in your bedroom? Write *Yes* or *No.*

Do you have a . . . in your bedroom?					
_____ Me _____ (name)					
_____ (name)					
_____ (name)					
_____ (name)					

33

In the Bathroom

bath mat	shampoo	toilet paper	flush the toilet
bathtub	shower	toothbrush	take a bath
brush	sink	toothpaste	take a shower
comb	soap	towel	wash your hands
mirror	toilet	washcloth	

A **Complete the story. Write the missing words.**

Everything went wrong in the

bathroom this morning. The water in the

1. _____shower_____ was cold!

I wanted to wash my body but there

wasn't any 2. _____.

Then the  3. _____ was wet. I couldn't find

a 4. _____. I used a

5. _____. The brush got stuck in my hair. Then I tried

to brush my teeth, but my  6. _____ fell

down the 7. _____. What a day!

B Do you use it for hair, teeth, or the whole body?

comb		

C Say the words. Circle the two words that start with the same sound.

1.

4.

2.

5.

3.

D Write six things you used in the bathroom this morning.

1. _____mirror_____   4. _____

2. _____   5. _____

3. _____   6. _____

Outside the House

address	gate	neighbor	tricycle
chimney	helmet	porch	wagon
door	house	roof	window
driveway	key	step	yard
fence	mail carrier	tree house	

A **Read and color.**

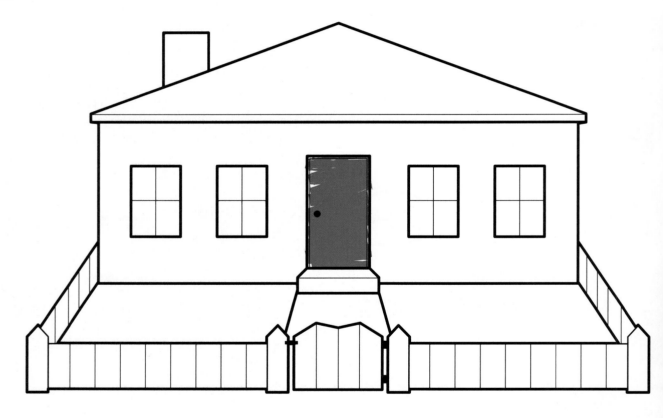

1. Color the door blue.

2. Color the windows yellow.

3. Color the step gray.

4. Color the chimney red.

5. Color the roof black.

6. Color the fence brown.

7. Color the gate purple.

8. Color the yard green.

B | Look at the pictures. Write the words for each thing.

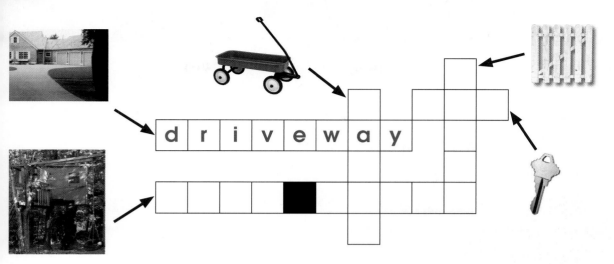

| d | r | i | v | e | w | a | y |

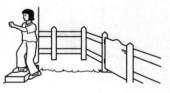

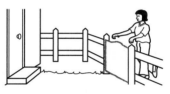

C | Which things are missing? Draw the missing thing. Write the word.

1. _____gate_____

2. _____

3. _____

Daniel Garcia

Brooklyn, New York

4. _____

5. _____

6. _____

D | (Circle) the correct spelling.

1. fenc (fence) fense

3. hoose house huse

2. rof ruf roof

4. wagun wegon wagon

In the Garage

battery	ladder	screwdriver
drill	lightbulb	tape measure
dryer	nail	washing machine
garbage can	paint	wrench
hammer	paintbrush	
iron	saw	

A **What is it? Write the word.**

1. ___wrench___   2. _____   3. _____

4. _____   5. _____   6. _____

B **Circle the first letter of each word.**

1. (p) w m   **2.** t s z   **3.** b l x   **4.** n b w

38

C **Write the word.**

1. <u>hammer</u>   2. _____   3. _____

4. _____   5. _____   6. _____

D **What does he need? Write the word.**

1. <u>washing machine</u>   2. _____   3. _____

4. _____   5. _____   6. _____

On the Move

airplane	ferry	ship	tunnel
airport	helicopter	skateboard	van
bike	hot air balloon	subway	wheelchair
bridge	motorcycle	taxi	
bus	road	train	
car	sailboat	truck	

A **Find the things that have wheels. Color them blue.**

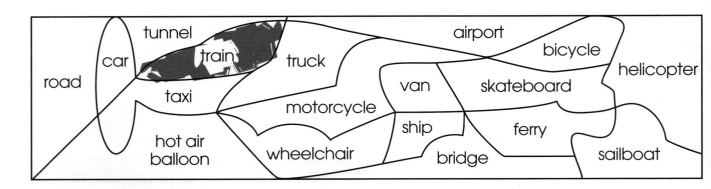

What do you see? _____

B **Find, circle, and write the words.**

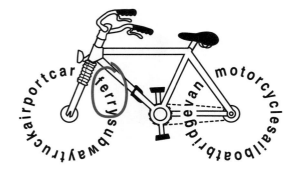

1. _____ferry_____   6. _____

2. _____   7. _____

3. _____   8. _____

4. _____   9. _____

5. _____

C Check (✓) the things you have been *in* or *on*.

- ☐ sailboat
- ☐ bus
- ✓ car
- ☐ ferry
- ☐ motorcycle

- ☐ taxi
- ☐ helicopter
- ☐ ship
- ☐ subway
- ☐ hot air balloon

- ☐ train
- ☐ truck
- ☐ van
- ☐ bicycle
- ☐ skateboard

D Match and write.

skate —— boat

wheel ——board

sail   plane

sub   way

air   port

air   chair

1. _____skateboard_____

2. _____

3. _____

4. _____

5. _____

6. _____

Around Town

ambulance   fire hydrant   museum
apartment building   fire station   post office
bakery   florist   school
bank   gas station   street
bus stop   hospital   supermarket
crosswalk   laundromat   theater
factory   mailbox   train station

A   Where can you get it? Write the answer.

1. __florist__   2. _____   3. _____

4. _____   5. _____   6. _____

B   Draw a circle around the things that begin with the letter *s*. Draw a square around the things that begin with the letter *f*.

C Complete the sentences. Write the missing words.

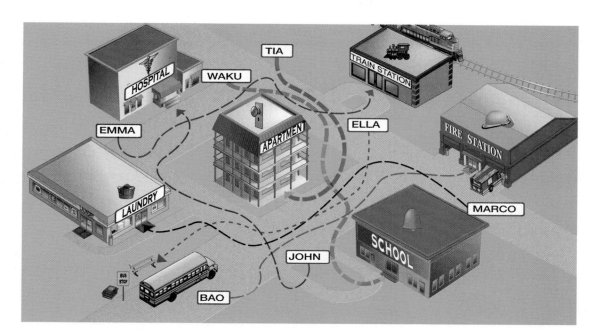

1. Tia is going to the _____ apartment building _____.

2. Waku is going to the _____.

3. John is going to the _____.

4. Ella is going to the _____.

5. Bao is going to the _____.

6. Emma is going to the _____.

7. Marco is going to the _____.

D Write three places you went this week.

1. _____

2. _____

3. _____

In the Park

ball	kite	playground	statue
bench	monkey bars	sandbox	swing
hill	path	seesaw	trash can
jump rope	picnic	slide	zoo

A **Where will Mike go? Write the word.**

1. He will pass a _____statue_____.

2. Then he will pass a _____.

3. Then he will pass a _____.

4. Then he will pass a mother and child flying a _____.

5. Then he will go up a _____.

6. Then he will pass people having a _____.

7. Finally, he will go into the _____.

B Check (✓) the words that begin with *s*.

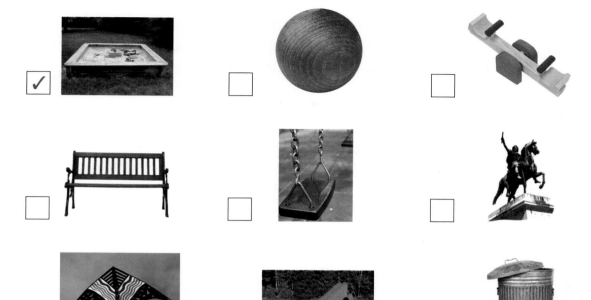

✓	☐	☐
☐	☐	☐
☐	☐	☐

C Ask your friends: What is your favorite thing in the playground? Check (✓) the boxes.

Name					
Me _____ (name)					
_____ (name)					
_____ (name)					
_____ (name)					

Run, Jump, Throw

catch	climb	hop	kick	push	run	swing
chase	fall	jump	pull	ride	slide	throw

A What can you do with it? (Circle.)

1. (push) (swing) climb

2. kick throw catch

3. jump ride climb

4.  run climb swing

5. ride push pull

6. hop slide jump

7. throw hop catch

8. pull ride kick

B What do you do with your arms? What do you do with your legs? Write.

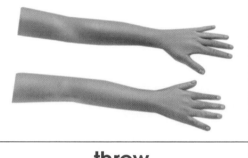

throw	

C Match and write the missing letters.

1. __t__ __h__ row

2. swi ____ ____

3. cat ____ ____

4. ____ ____ ase

5. ki ____ ____

6. pu ____ ____

At the Library

atlas	computer	library card	checkout
book	dictionary	magazine	return
bookshelf	DVD	newspaper	
checkout desk	librarian	videotape	

A **Write the word.**

1. ___librarian___   2. _____   3. _____

4. _____   5. _____   6. _____

B **Which can you read? Which can you watch? Write the answer.**

~~dictionary~~	magazine	DVD	newspaper
book	videotape	atlas	

Read	Watch
dictionary	

C **What begins with the letter you see?** (Circle) **the picture.**

1. C

2. B

3. D

4. V

5. L

D **Read and write the answer.**

1. People read this every day. It is black and white.

_____ **newspaper** _____

2. This person helps you at the library. _____

3. You need this to check out a library book.

_____

4. You can find your country in this book. _____

5. You can take books off of this. _____

6. You can find definitions of words in this. _____

7. You can check out a library book at this desk.

_____

Pets at the Vet

bird	collar	fur	paw	veterinarian
bone	dog	kitten	puppy	
cage	fish	leash	tail	
cat	fishbowl	mouse	turtle	

A **Count pets. Write the word for the pet.**

1. There are 6 _____fish_____.

2. There are 5 _____.

3. There are 4 _____.

4. There are 3 _____.

5. There are 2 _____.

6. There is 1 _____.

B **Write *Yes* or *No*.**

	has fur	has a tail	has paws	lives in a cage	can wear a collar
dog	Yes	Yes	Yes	No	Yes
mouse					
cat					
bird					
turtle					

C **Match the pets with their names. (Hint: Look at the first letter of the pet and the first letter of its name!)**

1. __Duke__   **2.** _____   **3.** _____

4. _____   **5.** _____

     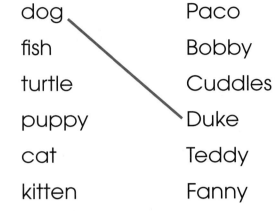

6. _____   **7.** _____

dog   Paco
fish   Bobby
turtle   Cuddles
puppy   Duke
cat   Teddy
kitten   Fanny
bird   Kitty

D **Write your answers for you and one friend.**
- **Do you have any pets? Write *Yes* or *No*.**
- **What kind of pets? Write.**
- **What pets are best? Write.**

Who?	Pets at home?	What kind?	3 best pets
__Me__ (name)			
_____ (name)			

At the Mall

ATM   electronics store   pet shop
bag   elevator   restrooms
bookstore   escalator   shoe store
candy store   food court   shopper
cell phone   movie theater   toy store
clothing store   music store

A Where did this shopper go? Write the shop.

2. _____
3. _____
1. <u>pet shop</u>
5. _____
4. _____
6. _____

52

B Where can you find these things in the mall?

1. _____ATM_____

2. _____

3. _____

4. _____

ADMIT
ONE
7452015   7452015

5. _____

6. _____

C Match and write the missing letters.

1. sh _____ pp _____ r

2. _____ l _____ vator

3. b _____ g

4. c _____ ll ph _____ n _____

5. __e__ sc __a__ l __a__ tor

D Write the answers. Ask your friends.

> What is your favorite place at the mall?

> My favorite place is the __bookstore__.

1. My favorite place at the mall is the _____.

2. _____'s favorite place is the _____.

3. _____'s favorite place is the _____.

At the Restaurant

bowl	cup	menu	spoon	pass
chair	fork	napkin	table	pour
chef	glass	plate	tablecloth	serve
chopsticks	knife	saucer	waiter	stir

A   **Read and color.**

The plate is purple.   The cup and saucer are red.

The spoon is orange.   The fork is green.

The knife is black.   The bowl is yellow.

The napkin is brown.   The glass is blue.

The menu is pink.

B Write the verbs.

stir
_____

C Look at the shape of each word. Find the boxes each word fits into. Write the word and draw a picture of each thing.

| knife | spoon | ~~plate~~ | table | chair | glass |

1. p l a t e

2.

3.

4.

5.

6.

55

baby	child	pacifier	rattle
baby wipes	crib	parent	stroller
bib	diaper	playpen	
bottle	high chair	potty chair	

A Write the words.

1. _____ baby _____

2. _____

3. _____

4. _____

5. _____

6. _____

B What is the first letter? Write each word in the correct column.

p	b
playpen	

C Find, (circle,) and write the words.

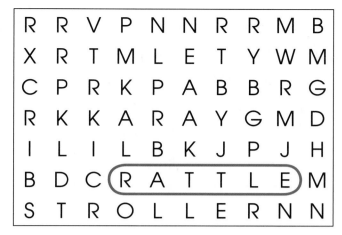

R	R	V	P	N	N	R	R	M	B
X	R	T	M	L	E	T	Y	W	M
C	P	R	K	P	A	B	B	R	G
R	K	K	A	R	A	Y	G	M	D
I	L	I	L	B	K	J	P	J	H
B	D	C	R	A	T	T	L	E	M
S	T	R	O	L	L	E	R	N	N

1. _____rattle_____   4. _____

2. _____   5. _____

3. _____   6. _____

D Put the words from Activity C in ABC order.

1. _____baby_____   4. _____

2. _____   5. _____

3. _____   6. _____

At the Construction Site

backhoe	electrician	saw	climb
bulldozer	hammer	shovel	dig
carpenter	hard hat	wire	hammer
crane	pipe		measure
dump truck	plumber		saw

A **Connect the dots. Write the words.**

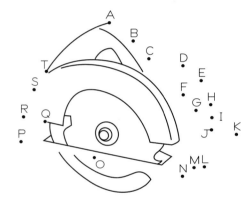

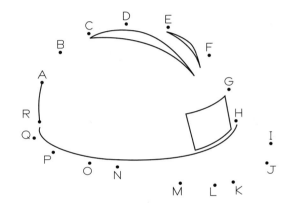

1. _____ saw _____

2. _____

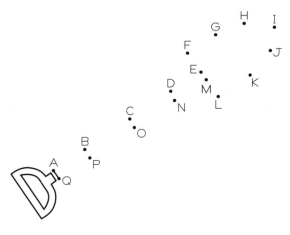

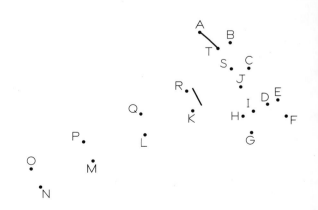

3. _____

4. _____

B **What can you do with it? Write.**

1. ____climb____

2. _____

3. _____

4. _____

5. _____

C **What is wrong with this picture? Write.**

1. The _____crane_____ is lifting a person.

2. The _____ is pink.

3. The _____ is dumping soccer balls.

4. The _____ is broken.

5. The dog has the _____.

6. The plumber's _____ is too small.

At the Doctor's Office

blood	medicine	scale	X-ray
chart	nurse	shot	
cut	patient	stethoscope	
doctor	prescription	stitches	

A   **Look at the picture. Circle Yes or No.**

1. The doctor is wearing a stethoscope.	Yes	No
2. The doctor is writing a prescription.	Yes	No
3. The doctor is looking at an X-ray.	Yes	No
4. The doctor is holding a chart.	Yes	No
5. The nurse is giving the patient a shot.	Yes	No
6. The nurse is giving the patient stitches.	Yes	No
7. The patient is a girl.	Yes	No
8. There is a scale in the office.	Yes	No
9. The patient is on the scale.	Yes	No

B Which one doesn't belong? Write the word.

1. ___doctor___

2. _____   3. _____

4. _____   5. _____

C (Circle) Yes or No.

1. Did you ever go to a doctor's office?   Yes   No

2. Did you ever get a cut?   Yes   No

3. Did you ever get a shot?   Yes   No

4. Did you ever get stitches?   Yes   No

5. Did you ever take medicine?   Yes   No

In the Waiting Room

bandage   earache   thermometer   cough

bump   fever   tissues   sneeze

cast   sore throat

crutches   stomachache

A   Write *Yes, he does* or *No, he doesn't.*

Kazu

Dario

1. Does Kazu have a fever? _____ <u>Yes, he does.</u> _____

2. Does Kazu have an earache? _____

3. Does Kazu have a stomachache? _____

4. Does Dario have an earache? _____

5. Does Dario have a sore throat? _____

6. Does Dario have a bump on his head? _____

B Unscramble and write the word.

 1.   momthereter   _____thermometer_____

 2.   stca   _____

 3.   checruts   _____

4.   gebanda   _____

5.   suetiss   _____

C Do the words start with the same sound? Circle Yes or No.

1. Yes / No

2. Yes / No

3. Yes / No

4. Yes / No

5. Yes / No

Jobs

actor	firefighter	plumber	truck driver
baker	hairstylist	police officer	
carpenter	painter	rock star	
dentist	pilot	scientist	

A Who uses it? Write.

1. __plumber__

2. _____

3. _____

4. _____

5. _____

6. _____

B Who works here? Write.

1. __firefighter__

2. _____

3. _____

4. _____

5. _____

C **Write sentences.**

Karen   Akira   Coco   John   Hector

1. _____ Karen is a police officer. _____

2. _____

3. _____

4. _____

5. _____

D **Match and write.**

truck _____ driver _____

hair_____

fire_____

police _____

rock _____

officer

stylist

star

~~driver~~

fighter

E **What are the three best jobs?**

1. _____

2. _____

3. _____

In My Classroom

alphabet	chair	desk	map	teacher
backpack	chalk	eraser	poster	wastebasket
blackboard	clock	globe	student	

A **Write the words. Find the hidden word in yellow.**

 __w__ __a__ __s__ __t__ __e__ __b__ __a__ __s__ __k__ __e__ __t__

 ___ ___ ___ ___ ___ ___

 ___ ___ ___ ___ ___ ___ ___ ___

___ ___ ___ ___ ___ ___ ___

___ ___ ___ ___ ___

 ___ ___ ___ ___

What is the hidden word?

Write your answer here:

_____

 ___ ___ ___ ___ ___ ___

66

B Do these words begin with the same letter? Write *Yes* or *No*.

1. __No__　　　2. _____　　　3. _____　　　4. _____

C Write the words.

1. things that show places: _____ globe _____ _____
2. things to sit and write on: _____ _____
3. things for a blackboard: _____ _____
4. people in my classroom: _____ _____

D What is wrong? Write.

1. The _____ chair _____ is broken.
2. The _____ is purple.
3. The _____ is square.
4. The _____ has no numbers.

Read, Write, Spell

build	give	open	spell	talk
close	listen	read	stand up	think
count	look at	sit down	take	write

A Write the word that fits in the boxes. Match the words to the pictures.

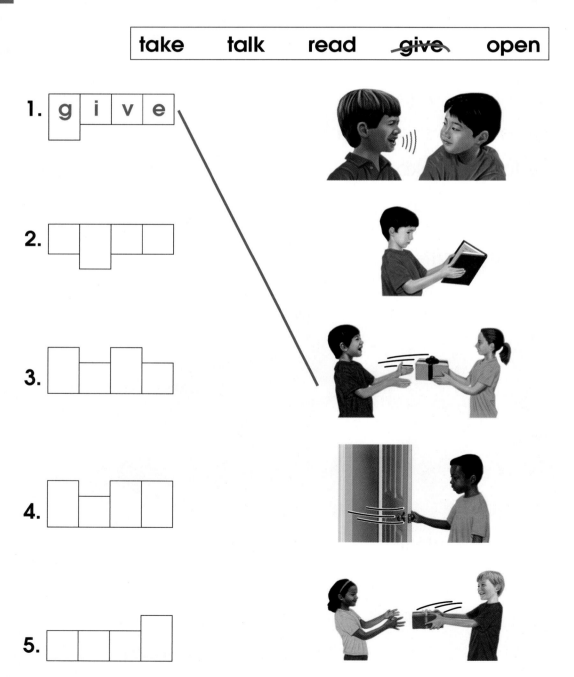

take   talk   read   ~~give~~   open

1. g i v e

2.

3.

4.

5.

68

B **What can you do with it?** **Circle.**

1.    stand up   (read)   spell

2.   listen   talk   sit down

3.   build   talk   spell

4. 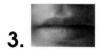   think   write   build

5.   talk   open   read

6.   give   sit down   take

7.   spell   open   close

8. ———   read   stand up   write

C **Write *Yes, I can* or *No, I can't.***

1. Can you count to 50? _____

   (Yes? Count to 50 for your friend.)

2. Can you spell your name? _____

   (Yes? Spell your name for your friend.)

3. Can you write with your left hand? _____

   (Yes? Write with your left hand for your friend.)

In My Schoolbag

binder	notebook	pencil case	ruler
calculator	paper	pencil sharpener	stapler
eraser	pen	pocket folder	textbook
money	pencil	report card	

A **Find the things that begin with the letter _p_. Color them red.**

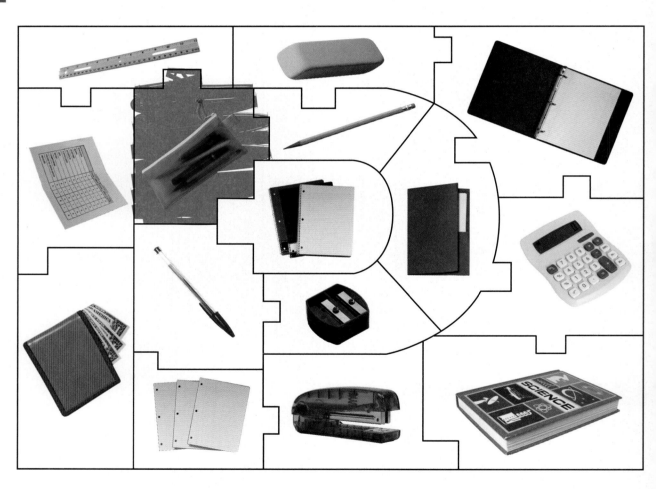

What letter do you see? _____

B Write the correct word.

1. You can use this to buy things. ____**money**____

2. You can use this to add numbers.

   _____

3. You can use this to write. _____

4. You can use this to fix a mistake. _____

5. You can put pencils in this. _____

6. You can put papers in this. _____

7. You can write in this. _____

C Ask friends: What is in your schoolbag? Check (✓) the boxes.

Do you have a . . .				
_____ (name)				
_____ (name)				
_____ (name)				
_____ (name)				

Arts and Crafts

beads	glue	ribbon	color
clay	markers	scissors	cut
construction paper	paint	tape	draw
craft stick	paintbrush	yarn	glue
crayons	pipe cleaners		paint

A **Look at the pictures. Write what each person is using.**

Karen

Ines

Joe

Amato

Gita

Tan

1. Karen is using __pipe cleaners__. **4.** Amato is using _____.

2. Ines is using _____. **5.** Gita is using _____.

3. Joe is using _____. **6.** Tan is using _____.

B **What can you do with it? Write.**

1.  _____ draw _____

2. _____

3. _____

4. _____

5. _____

72

C What is the first letter? Write each word in the correct column.

c	p
construction paper	

D What is it made of?

1. __construction paper__ __tape__

2. _____ _____

3. _____ _____

4. _____ _____

5. _____ _____

Musical Instruments

accordion	flute	recorder	trumpet
castanets	guitar	saxophone	tuba
cymbals	harmonica	tambourine	violin
drum	piano	triangle	xylophone

A **What is the instrument? Write the missing letters.**

1. __p__ ian __o__

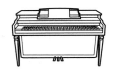

2. _____ ccor _____ ion

3. _____ ub _____

4. _____ uita _____

5. _____ am _____ ourine

6. _____ io _____ in

B **Write the instruments in the correct place.**

Instruments you hit	Instruments you blow into	Instruments with strings
	trumpet	

C Match the instruments and the people. (Hint: Look at the first letters!) Write the names in the correct places.

_____

_____

____Carmen____

_____

castanets — Diego

trumpet — Carmen

drum — Taro

recorder — Hisa

harmonica — Sun-ah

saxophone — Robbie

_____   _____

D Write the instruments from Activity C in ABC order.

1. _____castanets_____   4. _____

2 _____   5. _____

3. _____   6. _____

E What do you think? Write.

Which instrument is hard to play? _____

Which instrument is easy to play? _____

Which instrument is fun to play? _____

Fruit

apple	dates	orange	raisins
avocado	grapes	papaya	raspberries
banana	kiwi	peach	strawberries
blueberries	lemon	pear	
cherries	mango	pineapple	
coconut	melon	plum	

A **What fruit do you see? Write the name of the fruit.**

_____

_____

_____

_____

_____

B **What is it? Write the name of the fruit and color it.**

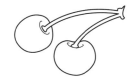   

1. <u>cherries</u>   2. _____   3. _____   4. _____

  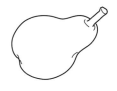

5. _____   6. _____   7. _____   8. _____

C Say the words. Do the words start with the same sound? (Circle) *Yes* or *No.*

1. (Yes) / No

2. Yes / No

3. Yes / No

4. Yes / No

5. Yes / No

6. Yes / No

7. Yes / No

8. Yes / No

D Write about you and a friend.

1. _____**Carmen**_____ likes to eat _____**strawberries**_____ and

_____**plums**_____ .

2. I like to eat _____ and _____ .

3. _____ likes to eat _____ and

_____ .

4. _____ likes to eat _____ and

_____ .

Vegetables

asparagus	celery	garlic	peas
broccoli	chili	green beans	pepper
cabbage	corn	lettuce	potato
carrot	cucumber	mushroom	tomato
cauliflower	eggplant	onion	zucchini

A **Look at the faces. Write the vegetables you see.**

<u>cauliflower</u>

_____

_____

_____

_____

_____

_____

_____

B **Write the missing double letter.**

1. pe __p__ __p__ er   **4.** ca ____ ____ age

2. le ____ ____ uce   **5.** ca ____ ____ ot

3. bro ____ ____ oli   **6.** e ____ ____ plant

C Write the vegetable on the right color.

asparagus

_____

_____

_____

_____

_____

_____

D Do you like these vegetables? Check (✓) the vegetables you like and don't like.

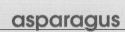

	I like it!	I don't like it!
broccoli		
corn		
mushroom		
potato		
celery		
pepper		

Food 1

beans   chicken   meat   rice   sugar
bread   egg   noodles   salad
butter   fish   nuts   salt
cereal   honey   pasta   soup
cheese   jam   pepper   spaghetti

A   **Write the name of the food you see under the picture of the *fork*, *spoon*, or *knife*.**

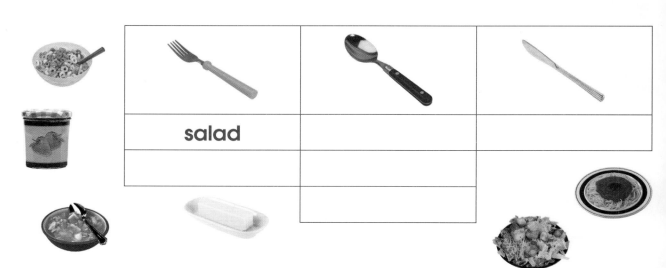

🍴 fork	🥄 spoon	🔪 knife
salad		

B   **Which word doesn't belong? (Circle) and write the word.**

1.   <u>   **noodles**   </u>   2.   _____

3.   _____   4.   _____

C Which foods can you find in a refrigerator?

jam

D Match and write the missing letters.

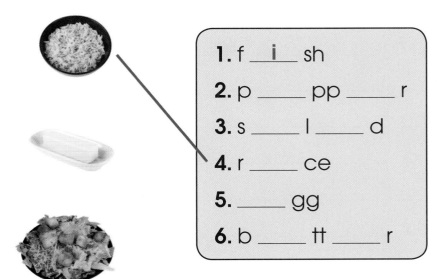

1. f __i__ sh

2. p _____ pp _____ r

3. s _____ l _____ d

4. r _____ ce

5. _____ gg

6. b _____ tt _____ r

Food 2

chocolate   hamburger   pie   taco
coffee   ice cream   pizza   tea
cookie   juice   sandwich   water
egg roll   kebab   soda
french fries   milk   sushi

A   **Match the children to the foods they are eating.**

Yumiko   Allen   Carmen

David   Chim

Sarah   Emil   Mary

1. Yumiko is eating a _____**sandwich**_____.

2. Allen is eating _____.

3. Carmen is eating a _____.

4. David is eating a _____.

5. Chim is eating _____.

6. Sarah is eating a _____.

7. Emil is eating _____.

8. Mary is eating _____.

B **Write the words.**

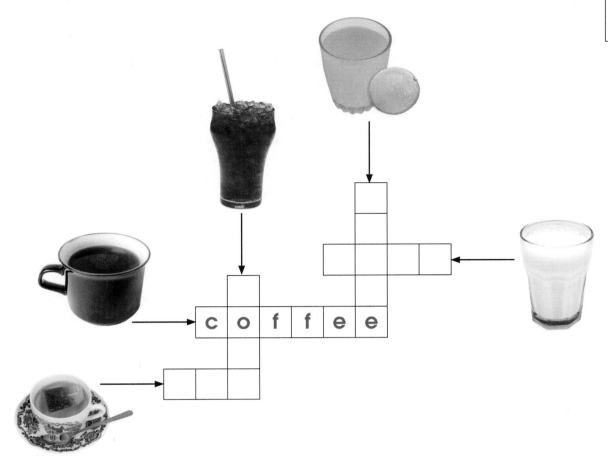

c	o	f	f	e	e

C **Complete the sentences about foods.**

1. I like _____.

2. I don't like _____.

3. I put _____ on my bread.

4. I put salt on _____.

5. I eat a _____ for lunch.

Story Time 1

carriage	fairy godmother	magic wand	queen
castle	flag	prince	throne
crown	king	princess	tower

A **Find the words for people. Color them yellow.**

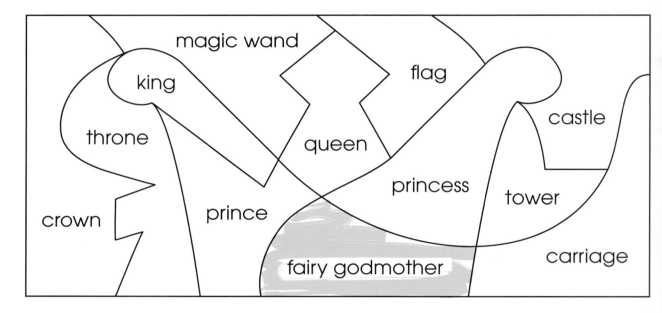

magic wand

king

flag

throne

castle

queen

princess

tower

crown

prince

fairy godmother

carriage

What do you see? _____

B **Find and circle the words.**

T	T	O	W	E	R
H	C	G	N	X	W
R	R	K	I	N	G
O	O	P	N	W	G
N	W	G	V	T	Y
E	N	F	L	A	G

84

C **Complete the story. Write the missing words.**

A long time ago there was a 1. ___king___

and a 2. _____. They had no children. One

day, the king said to his 3. _____, "I want a son

and a daughter." She waved her 4. _____

at a frog. It became a 5. _____. Then the

6. _____ waved her 7. _____

at another frog. It became a 8. _____.

The 9. _____ was happy. But the

10. _____ did not like wearing a

11. _____, and the 12. _____ did

not like living in a 13. _____. So they asked

the 14. _____ to make them frogs again!

85

broom	fairy	giant	treasure chest
dragon	flying carpet	knight	witch
dwarf	forest	magic lamp	wizard
elf	genie	sword	

A **What do you see? Write the words.**

treasure chest _____ _____

_____ _____ _____

_____ _____

B **Circle the first letter of each word in the picture.**

1. (d) p **2.** m w **3.** j g **4.** f p

C **Complete the story. Write the missing words.**

One day, a **1.** _____knight_____, a

 2. _____, and a **3.** _____

were in a **4.** _____. They found a

 5. _____ and opened it. Inside, they found

a **6.** _____, a **7.** _____, and

a **8.** _____. The **9.** _____

took the **10.** _____ and flew away. The

 11. _____ took the **12.** _____

and flew away. The **13.** _____ took the

 14. _____ and walked deep into the

 15. _____ to look for another

 16. _____.

Toys and Games

action figure	computer game	monster
blocks	crayons	puppet
board game	dice	puzzle
boat	dinosaur	robot
bubbles	doll	teddy bear
coloring book	dollhouse	train
comic book	fire truck	yo-yo

A **Read and color.**

The robot is yellow.

The yo-yo is pink.

The boat is purple.

The teddy bear is brown.

The blocks are blue.

The train is black.

The dinosaur is green.

The fire truck is red.

B **Match and write.**

action	book
coloring	book
comic	house
doll	figure
computer	game
fire	game
teddy	truck
board	bear

1. _____action figure_____ 5. _____

2. _____ 6. _____

3. _____ 7. _____

4. _____ 8. _____

C **Which letter does it start with? Write each word in the correct column.**

b	d
blocks	

Birthday Party

balloon	card	popcorn	bake
bow	cupcake	potato chips	blow out
cake	friends	present	light
candle	invitation	wrapping paper	share
candy	lollipop		wrap

A **Count and write the number.**

1. friends __6__

2. cakes ____

3. candles ____

4. cupcakes ____

5. bowls of potato chips ____

6. bowls of popcorn ____

7. presents ____

8. balloons ____

B **Check (✓) the words that begin with a _c_.**

Complete the story. Write the missing words.

Every year I have a birthday party. I invite

my friends. On my birthday, my parents put

1. ____**balloons**____ around the house and

2. _____ presents in

3. _____. Then my

4. _____ come to our house and we

have a party! My friends usually bring

5. _____. My mom and dad bake me a

6. _____. Then they

7. _____ the 8. _____.

Everybody sings "Happy Birthday." Then I

9. _____ the 10. _____.

I love my birthday!

At the Beach

beach ball	kite	sandcastle	sun hat
beach chair	ocean	seagull	sunscreen
cooler	pail	shell	surfboard
flippers	sailboat	shovel	wave
island	sand	snorkel	

A **Write the word for each thing.**

3. _____

5. _____

4. _____

1. beach chair

7. _____

2. _____

6. _____

B Unscramble the words and match.

1. _____

2. _____

3. _____

1. boarfdsur
2. ellsh
3. vewa
4. stlendsaca
5. dlanis
6. teki

4. _____

5. **surfboard**

6. _____

C Do you use it in the ocean or on the sand? Write.

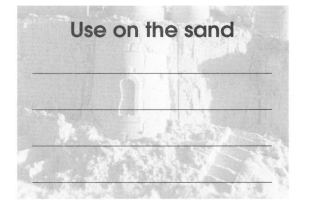

Use in the ocean

_____ sailboat _____

_____

_____

Use on the sand

_____

_____

_____

At the Fairgrounds

acrobat   cotton candy   roller coaster
carnival   Ferris wheel   ticket
carousel   fireworks   tightrope walker
circus   juggler   trapeze
clown   lion tamer

A   **Write the missing words.**

1. The _____**clown**_____ is
   on a _____. He
   is eating _____.

2. The _____ and
   the _____
   are on a _____.

3. The _____
   is on the _____.
   He has a _____
   in his hand.

94

B What is it? Write the word.

1. ___juggler___   2. _____   3. _____

4. _____   5. _____   6. _____

C Unscramble and write the word.

1. ___circus___   2. _____   3. _____

4. _____   5. _____   6. _____

At the Street Fair

artist   painting   clap

camera   photographer   dance

dancer   puppet show   paint

magician   singer   play a guitar

microphone   sing

musician   take a picture

A   **Look at the pictures. Write the word for the action.**

1. _____**sing**_____

2. _____

3. _____

4. _____

5. _____

6. _____

B Which person uses it? Write the person.

1. _____artist_____   2. _____   3. _____

4. _____   5. _____   6. _____

C Which words end with the letters *er?* (Circle) them.

On the Farm

barn	chicken	goat	pig	sheep
bull	cow	hay	piglet	tractor
calf	donkey	horse	rooster	turkey
chick	farmer	lamb	scarecrow	

A **What's wrong with this picture? Write.**

1. The _____pig_____ is wearing glasses.

2. The _____ is driving the tractor.

3. The farmer is talking to the _____.

4. There is a _____ on the farmer's head.

5. The _____ is purple.

6. The goat is on top of the _____.

B **Which has four legs? Which has wings? Write.**

4 legs	wings
goat	

C **Write the word that fits in the boxes. Match the words to the pictures.**

barn	goat	lamb	calf	~~bull~~

1. b u l l

2.

3.

4.

5.

Camping

campfire	flashlight	raft	tent
canoe	life jacket	river	trail
compass	matches	rope	trailer
east	mountain	sleeping bag	waterfall
fishing pole	north	south	west

A Alex is camping. What does he need? Write the word.

1. ___fishing pole___

2. _____

3. _____

4. _____

5. _____

6. _____

B Complete with a word from the box.

1. fishing _____ **pole** _____

2. camp_____

3. sleeping _____

4. life _____

5. flash_____

6. water_____

jacket

~~pole~~

fall

light

bag

fire

C Complete the story. Write the missing words.

Last night was exciting. My father and I slept

in a 1. __ **sleeping bag** __. We were in a

2. _____ all night. When it was dark,

I used a 3. _____. My father made a

4. _____ with 5. _____.

It was fun! But there wasn't a 6. _____.

There wasn't a 7. _____. There wasn't a

8. _____. Why? Because we were in our yard!

Sports

baseball   hockey stick   soccer ball
basketball   hoop   tennis
bat   karate   tennis ball
glove   net   tennis racket
goal   rollerblade
hockey   rollerblading   baseball (the sport)
hockey puck   soccer   basketball (the sport)

A   **Count the things for sports. Write the number.**

1. There are __4__ baseballs.

2. There are _____ hockey pucks.

3. There are _____ soccer balls.

4. There are _____ tennis balls.

5. There are _____ basketballs.

6. There is _____ tennis racket.

B Match and write the missing letters.

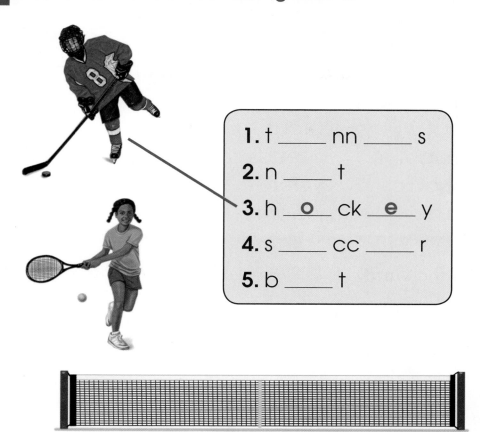

1. t ____ nn ____ s
2. n ____ t
3. h __o__ ck __e__ y
4. s ____ cc ____ r
5. b ____ t

C What do you use for this sport? Circle.

1. hockey   **2.** tennis

3. basketball   **4.** soccer   **5.** baseball

Spring

bud	grass	rainbow	watering can
bush	lawn mower	rainy	
cloud	leaf	root	dig
cloudy	mud	seeds	plant
flower	puddle	stem	water
garden	rain	warm	

A **What is it? Write the word.**

1. _____

2. _____

3. _____

4. _____

5. _____

6. _____

7. _____

B **Which word doesn't belong? Circle.**

1. dig   plant   (puddle)

2. rainbow   cloud   mud

3. rainy   lawn mower   cloudy

4. warm   flower   bush

5. watering can root   stem

C Draw a flower. Write the words where they belong on the flower: *stem, leaf, bud, root.*

D Circle the correct spelling.

1.  grays   gras   (grass)

2. watr   water   watter

3. puddle   pudel   puddel

4. seds   seyds   seeds

5. jarden   garden   gardin

6. clod   kloud   cloud

Summer

barbecue grill   lifeguard   swim ring   dive
bathing suit   pool   water wings float
fan   sun   watermelon splash
hot   sunglasses   swim
ice cream cone   sunny

A   **What is it? Write the word.**

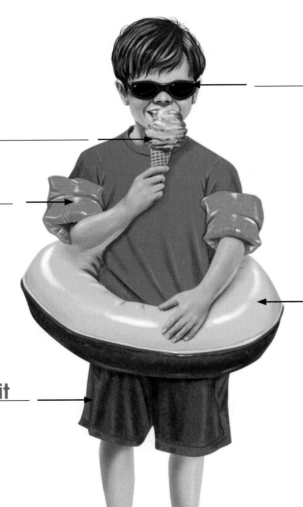

bathing suit

B Complete the sentences. Write the missing word.

1. You swim in a _____**pool**_____.

2. People wear a _____ in a pool.

3. A _____ can help you swim.

4. A _____ watches you when you swim.

5. When you throw water at someone, you _____.

6. When you _____, you jump in a pool.

7. When you _____, you rest at the top of the water.

C Complete with a word from the box.

1. swim _____**ring**_____

2. ice cream _____

3. barbecue _____

4. water _____

5. bathing _____

6. life_____

7. water_____

8. sun_____

grill	~~ring~~
guard	glasses
cone	melon
wings	suit

Fall

broom	pumpkin	wheelbarrow	rake
cool	rake	wind	ride a bike
costume	school bus	windy	skateboard
leaf	sweep		sweep
pile	tree		

A Write the word that fits in the boxes. Match the words to the pictures.

pile   ~~rake~~   tree   wind   leaf

1. | r | a | k | e |

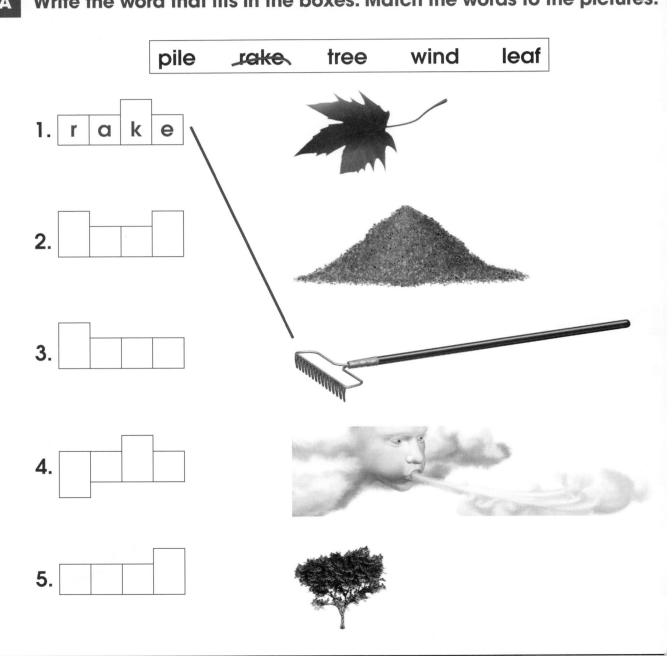

2.

3.

4.

5.

B **Connect the dots. Write the word.**

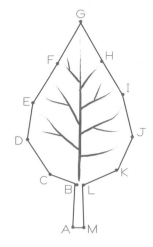

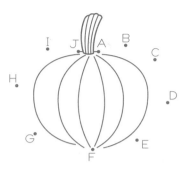

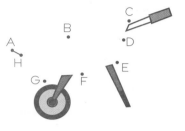

1. _____leaf_____   2. _____   3. _____

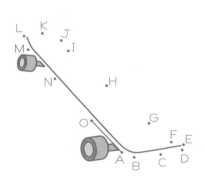

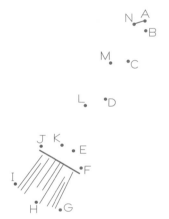

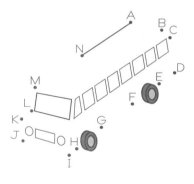

4. _____   5. _____   6. _____

C **Which word doesn't belong? (Circle.)**

1. rake   (tree)   broom

2. sweep   rake   pumpkin

3. school bus   skateboard   sweep

4. pile   skateboard   ride a bike

5. cool   wheelbarrow   windy

6. costume   tree   leaf

Winter

Christmas tree   Santa Claus   snowboard
cold   skis   snowflake
ice   sled   snowing
ice skates   snow   snowman
icicle   snow angel
mittens   snowball

A   **Which words have *snow*? Circle.**

B What is missing? Write the word.

1. __snowboard__   2. _____   3. _____

4. _____   5. _____   6. _____

C Draw a picture of each word.

ice skates   snowman   mittens   Christmas tree

Bugs

ant	centipede	grasshopper	spider
bee	cocoon	ladybug	spider web
beetle	cricket	mosquito	tick
butterfly	dragonfly	moth	wasp
caterpillar	fly	snail	worm

A **Count the bugs. Write the number.**

1. __4__

2. _____

3. _____

4. _____

5. _____

6. _____

7. _____

8. _____

B **Write the word for each bug.**

1. I have eight legs. I make webs. I am a _____**spider**_____.

2. I am yellow and black. I like flowers. I am a _____.

3. I was a caterpillar. Now I have beautiful wings. I am a

   _____.

4. I am a big, green bug. I am a _____.

5. I am red with black spots. I am a _____.

6. I will be a butterfly one day. Now I am a _____.

C **Write the words.**

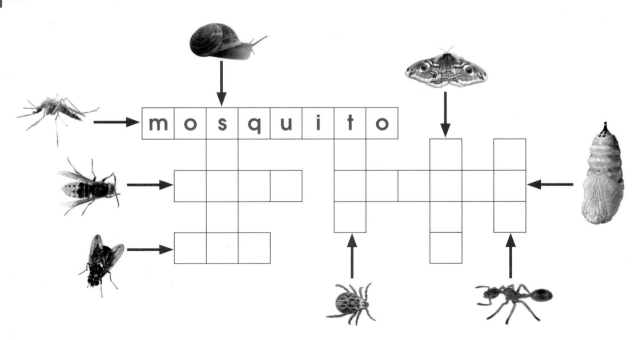

| m | o | s | q | u | i | t | o |

In the Rain Forest

bat	feather	hummingbird	peacock
beak	flamingo	monkey	tiger
chimpanzee	frog	orangutan	wing
crocodile	gorilla	parrot	

A Find the words *flamingo, parrot, peacock,* and *hummingbird.*
Color them yellow.

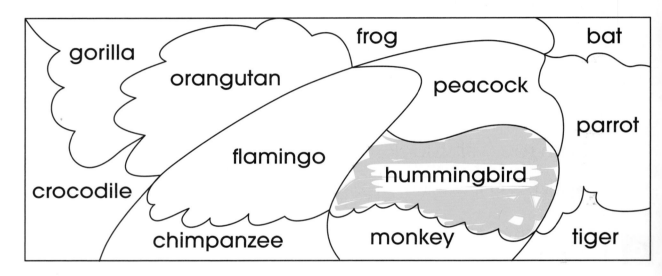

What do you see? _____

B Which word doesn't belong? Circle the word.

1. (frog)   wing   feather

2. monkey   tiger   chimpanzee

3. gorilla   bat   hummingbird

4. beak   wing   chimpanzee

5. parrot   flamingo   crocodile

C **What's wrong with this picture? Write.**

1. The _____**monkey**_____ has wings.

2. The _____ is flying.

3. The _____ is small.

4. The _____ is pink.

5. The _____ is in a tree.

6. The _____ has a beak.

D **Match and write the missing letters.**

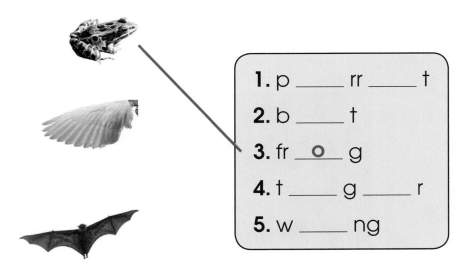

1. p ____ rr ____ t
2. b ____ t
3. fr __**o**__ g
4. t ____ g ____ r
5. w ____ ng

In the Grasslands

buffalo	horn	lion	stripes
elephant	kangaroo	ostrich	trunk
giraffe	koala	rhinoceros	tusk
hippopotamus	leopard	spots	zebra

A **Write the word for each animal.**

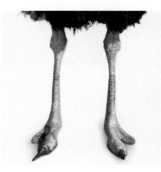

leopard

_____

_____

_____

_____

_____

_____

_____

B (Circle) the correct answer.

1. Does a giraffe have a long neck?   Yes, it does.

   No, it doesn't.

2. Does a zebra have stripes?   Yes, it does.

   No, it doesn't.

3. Does a lion have a horn?   Yes, it does.

   No, it doesn't.

4. Does a kangaroo have a tusk?   Yes, it does.

   No, it doesn't.

5. Does a leopard have spots?   Yes, it does.

   No, it doesn't.

6. Does an elephant have a trunk?   Yes, it does.

   No, it doesn't.

C Find, (circle,) and write the words.

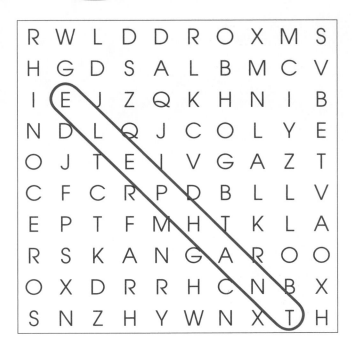

```
R  W  L  D  D  R  O  X  M  S
H  G  D  S  A  L  B  M  C  V
I  E  J  Z  Q  K  H  N  I  B
N  D  L  Q  J  C  O  L  Y  E
O  J  T  E  I  V  G  A  Z  T
C  F  C  R  P  D  B  L  L  V
E  P  T  F  M  H  T  K  L  A
R  S  K  A  N  G  A  R  O  O
O  X  D  R  R  H  C  N  B  X
S  N  Z  H  Y  W  N  X  T  H
```

_____ **elephant** _____

_____

_____

_____

_____

In the Sea

coral reef	fish	octopus	sea horse	starfish
crab	jellyfish	oyster	seaweed	stingray
dolphin	lobster	pearl	shark	turtle
fin	mussel	scales	shrimp	whale

A **Write the sea animals you see.**

1. _____stingray_____   5. _____

2. _____   6. _____

3. _____   7. _____

4. _____   8. _____

B Find, circle, and write the sea animals.

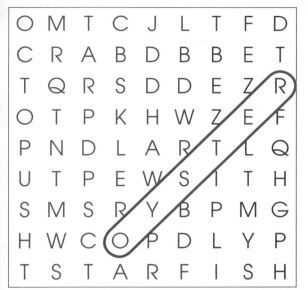

O	M	T	C	J	L	T	F	D
C	R	A	B	D	B	B	E	T
T	Q	R	S	D	D	E	Z	R
O	T	P	K	H	W	Z	E	F
P	N	D	L	A	R	T	L	Q
U	T	P	E	W	S	I	T	H
S	M	S	R	Y	B	P	M	G
H	W	C	O	P	D	L	Y	P
T	S	T	A	R	F	I	S	H

_____ **oyster** _____

_____

_____

_____

_____

_____

C Write the words in ABC order.

1. _____ **crab** _____

2. _____

3. _____

4. _____

5. _____

D Complete with a word from the box.

sea____ **weed** _____

sting_____

jelly_____

coral _____

star_____

reef

fish

fish

~~weed~~

ray

In the Woodlands

beaver	eagle	rabbit	squirrel
chipmunk	mouse	raccoon	toad
deer	nest	robin	woodpecker
duck	pond	skunk	

A Find, circle, and write the words.

1. _____ squirrel _____

2. _____

3. _____

4. _____

5. _____

6. _____

B Which words begin with the letter *r*? Check (✓) the words.

☐    ☐   ☐   ☐

✓   ☐    ☐    ☐

C **Where can you find each animal?**

	beaver	

D **Write the answers. Ask your friends.**

What is your favorite animal in the woodlands?

My favorite animal in the woodlands is ____a rabbit____.

1. My favorite animal in the woodlands is _____a rabbit_____.

2. _____'s favorite animal in the woodlands is

_____.

3. _____'s favorite animal in the woodlands is

_____.

4. _____'s favorite animal in the woodlands is

_____.

In the Polar Lands

antler	goose	penguin	walrus
cub	grizzly bear	polar bear	wolf
Eskimo	igloo	puffin	
flipper	lake	reindeer	
fox	moose	seal	

A **Unscramble and write the word.**

1

2

3

4

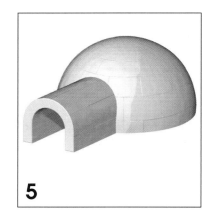

5

6

1. oosem _____**moose**_____

2. leas _____

3. ruswal _____

4. lfwo _____

5. oogli _____

6. buc _____

B Which animal begins with the letter you see? Circle.

1. F

2. P

3. G

4. R

5. W

C Which word doesn't belong? Circle the picture and write the word.

1. _____fox_____

2. _____

3. _____

4. _____

5. _____

6. _____

In the Desert

cactus	coyote	owl	sand dune	tortoise
camel	lizard	palm tree	scorpion	vulture
claws	oasis	rock	snake	

A **Complete the sentences. Write the missing word.**

1. The palm tree is in an _____**oasis**_____.

2. The _____ is under the palm tree.

3. The _____ is on the rock.

4. The _____ is next to the rock.

5. The _____ is in the cactus.

6. The _____ is next to the cactus.

7. The _____ is in the sky.

8. The _____ is near the sand dune.

B What is it? Write the word.

1. ___tortoise___

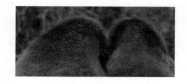

2. _____

3. _____

4. _____

5. _____

6. _____

C Find, circle, and write the words.

1. _____scorpion_____

2. _____

3. _____

4. _____

5. _____

6. _____

Space

astronaut   Mercury   satellite   sun
constellation   moon   Saturn   telescope
Earth   Neptune   spaceship   Uranus
Jupiter   planet   space station   Venus
Mars   rocket   star

A Write the word.

1.   satellite

2. _____

3. _____

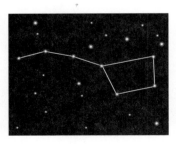

4. _____

5. _____

6. _____

7. _____

8. _____

B Unscramble and write the word.

1. netuNep
   _____Neptune_____

2. pitJuer
   _____

3. urSatn
   _____

4. snuVe
   _____

5. srMa
   _____

6. nusraU
   _____

7. rthEa
   _____

8. uryerMc
   _____

C Write the words from Activity B in ABC order.

1. _____Earth_____

2. _____

3. _____

4. _____

5. _____

6. _____

7. _____

8. _____

D Complete the story. Write the missing words.

Last night I went to the 1. _____moon_____

in a 2. _____ . I also visited the

3. _____ and a 4. _____ . Then I

came back to 5. _____ . Then I woke up!

Letters

Write the letters.

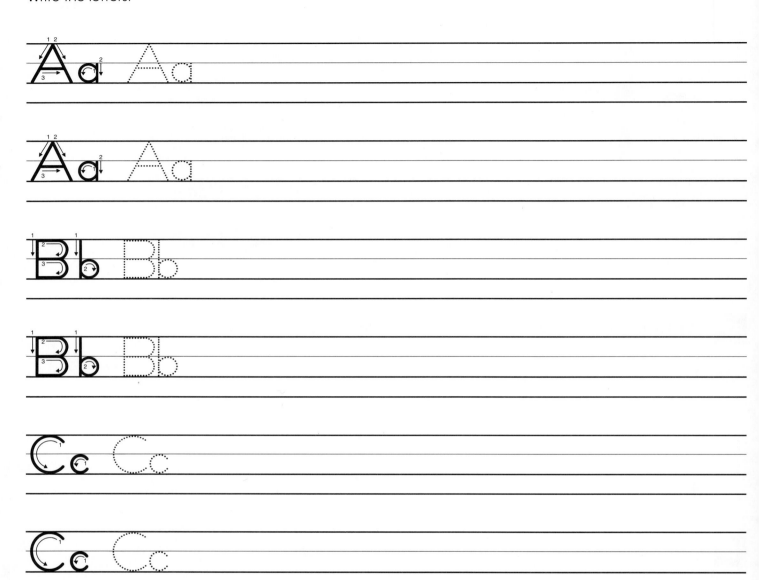

Letters

Write the letters.

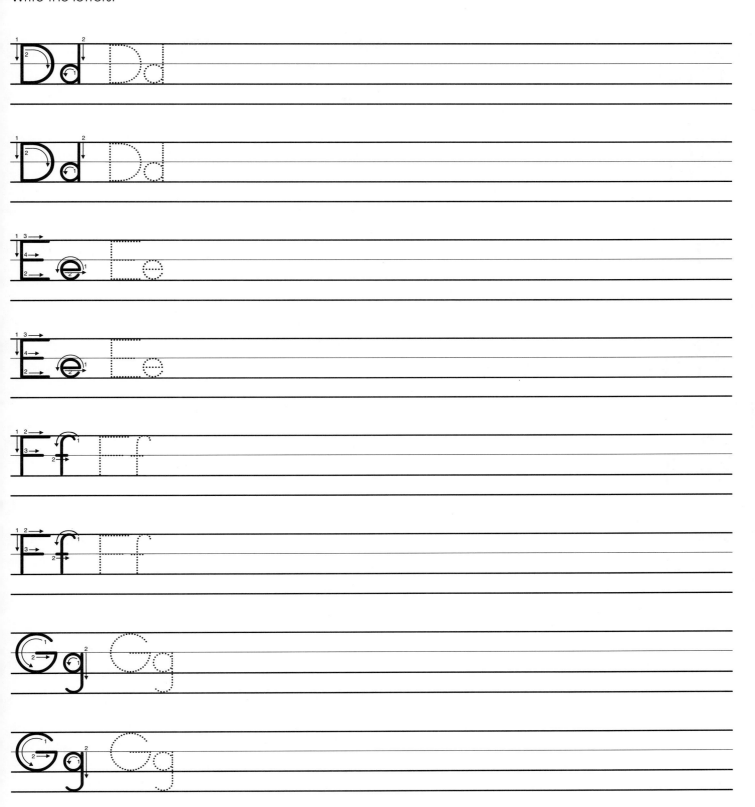

Letters

Write the letters.

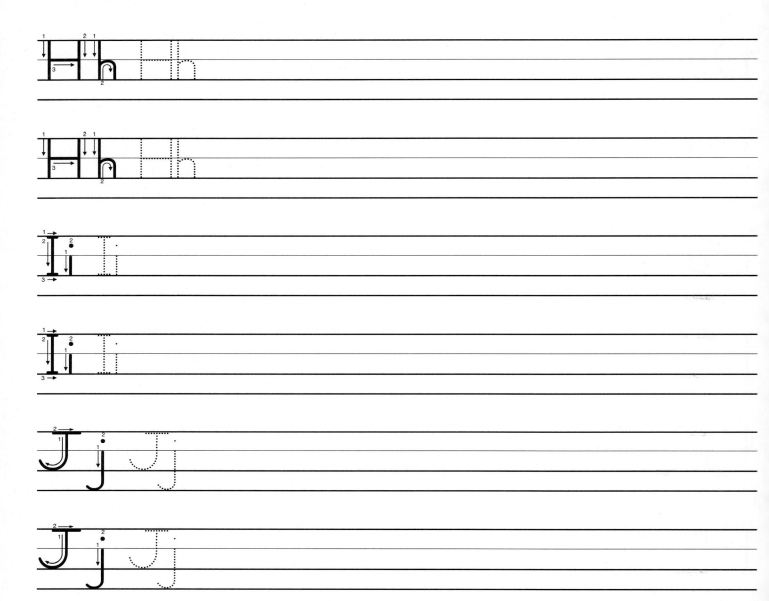

Letters

Write the letters.

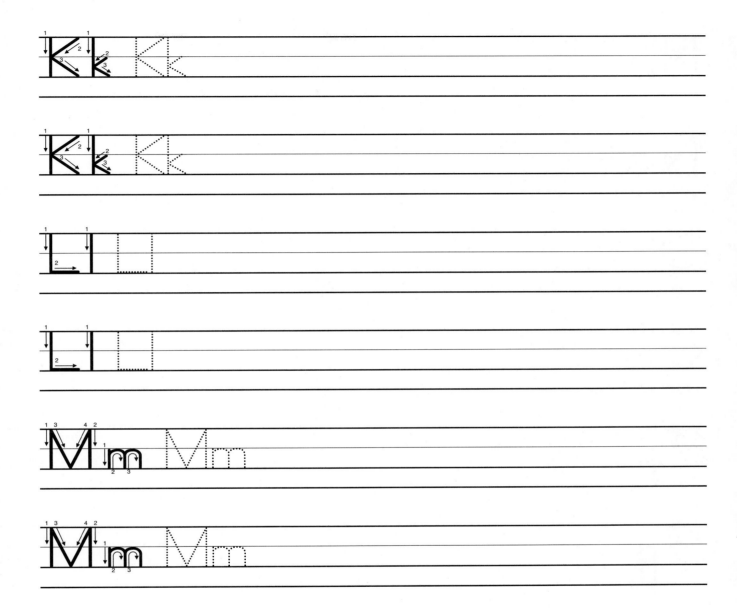

Letters

Write the letters.

N n　N n

N n　N n

O o　O o

O o　O o

P p　P p

P p　P p

Letters

Write the letters.

Q q   Q q

Q q   Q q

R r   R r

R r   R r

S s   S s

S s   S s

T t   T t

T t   T t

Letters

Write the letters.

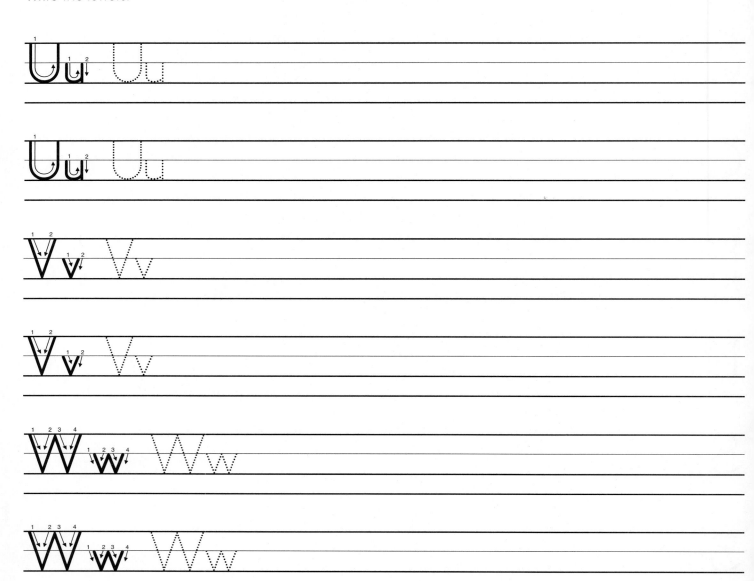

Letters

Write the letters.

Numbers

Write the numbers.

1   1

2   2

3   3

4   4

5   5

6   6

7   7

8   8

9   9

10   10

Numbers

Write the numbers.

11 11

12 12

13 13

14 14

15 15

16 16

17 17

18 18

19 19

20 20

Writing Practice